Robin Hood

Howard Pyle

Retold by

Ken Methold and Sheila Lyne

LEVEL 2

Robin Hood

Howard Pyle

Retold by Ken Methold and Sheila Lyne

Series Editor: Ken Methold
Acquisitions Editor: John Thomas
Copy Editors: Paul Edmunds, Nigel A. Caplan
Illustrator: Bun Heang Ung
Cover/Interior Design: Design Plus

http://www.compasspub.com
email: info@compasspub.com

9 10 11 12 13 14 15 - BA - 2015 2014 2013

ISBN: 978-1-59966-199-5

Printed in Korea

Contents

Robin Hood Meets the Outlaws

Preview Questions

1. Do you know who Robin Hood is?
2. In which country do you think Robin Hood lived?
3. What do you think this story will be about?

In England many years ago, there was a good king. His name was Richard, and the people loved him.

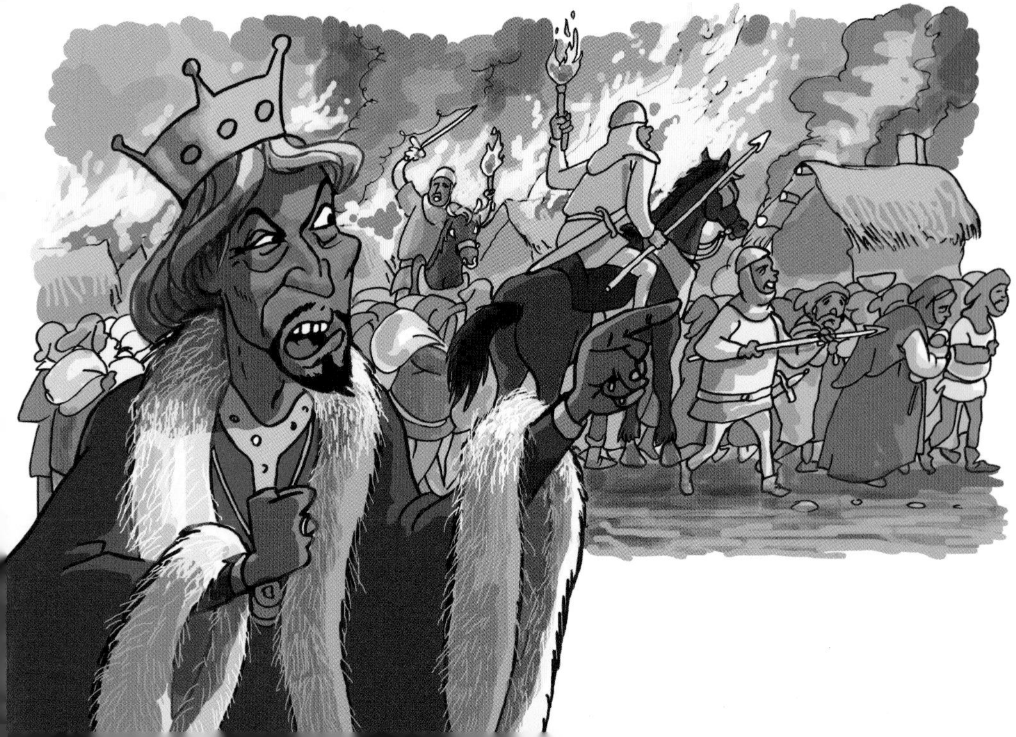

One day, King Richard left England. He had to fight in a war in another country. His brother, John, ruled in his place. Prince John was a bad man. He took away the houses and lands of the poor people and gave them to his friends. He killed anyone who did not obey him.

Many men had nowhere to live. Some of them lived in a forest. Prince John said they were **outlaws**. One of these men stood out from the rest.

"I was a rich man, and I gave to the poor," this man told the other men. "Prince John does not like me. He took my lands and gave them to his friends. Now he wants to kill me."

He turned to a beautiful woman who was standing by his side.

"This is Marion," he said. "She loves me, and I love her. Her father will not let her marry me. He is **afraid**

of Prince John, but one day we will be married."

"What is your name?" one of the men asked.

"Call me Robin Hood. It is not my real name, but it is the name you must use."

The men wanted a leader. They liked Robin Hood.

"We want you as our leader!" they **shouted.**

"Very well," Robin Hood replied. "I will be your leader. We will live together in the forest. We will all wear green clothes. We will stay here until good King Richard returns. He will give us back our lands and houses."

"We need some money, Robin," one of the men said. His name was Will. "I was your servant until Prince John took your lands. I hid some of your gold in your house before we left. Let me go to your house and get it."

"You must be careful, Will," Robin Hood said. "The sheriff obeys the prince. He will hang you if he catches you."

"I'll be careful, Robin," Will said. "I'll take Much with me."

Much was the youngest of the outlaws. He was a good and brave boy.

Will and Much went into the town. The sheriff's men were everywhere. They were looking for Robin Hood and the other outlaws.

Will and Much got into Robin's house without the sheriff's men seeing them. Will found the gold and put some of it in a bag. He gave this to Much. The boy ran off. Will put some gold and **jewels** under his clothes. Then he left the house.

Later, when Will came out of the house, the sheriff's men saw him. He tried to run away, but they caught him. They took him to the sheriff.

"Who are you? What were you doing in Robin Hood's house?" the sheriff asked him.

"I was his servant," Will said. "I was trying to get some of my things from his house."

"I have no **quarrel** with you," the sheriff said. "My quarrel is with Robin Hood. You may go."

Then one of then sheriff's men said, "How do we know the things are his? Perhaps they are Robin Hood's."

"You may be right," the sheriff said. "**Search** him!"

The men searched Will and found the gold.

"If you are a poor servant, then that gold must not be yours!" the Sheriff yelled angrily. "It is Robin Hood's.

You must be one of his men. You are an outlaw and you will hang tomorrow."

Much was waiting for Will in the forest. When Will did not come, Much went back into town. He met a friend.

"Where is Will?" he asked him.

"The sheriff's men took him," the friend answered. "The sheriff will hang him tomorrow."

Much ran back into the forest. He ran as fast as he could to the outlaws' camp.

"Will is in **prison**," he told Robin. "The sheriff will hang him tomorrow!"

"We must rescue Will," Robin said.

The next day Robin put on a **beggar's** old and dirty clothes. Then he went into town.

Robin waited near the **gallows**. A crowd of people was waiting. They wanted to see the hanging.

Soon the sheriff's men brought Will from the prison. The sheriff asked, "Where is the **hangman**? He should be here."

He sent one of his men to get the hangman. The man soon came back.

"The hangman is drunk," the man said. "He cannot

do his work."

The sheriff was very angry. "This outlaw must hang!" he shouted. "Who will do the hangman's work for a piece of gold?"

A beggar in the crowd put up his hand.

"I will," he said.

He walked toward the gallows.

"I will do anything for gold," he shouted. He put the rope around Will's neck. As he did so, he spoke quietly to him. "Don't be afraid, Will. You won't hang. I have a sword for you and another for me under my coat.

When I say 'Now!' take the sword from me, and we will fight our way through the sheriff's men."

"Be quick!" the sheriff shouted at the beggar. "Hang him and then we can all go."

"Now!" shouted Robin.

He took the two swords from under his coat. He gave one to Will and kept one for himself. They jumped at the sheriff's men. The men were too surprised to fight back.

Robin and Will ran out of town into the forest. There were horses waiting for them. They rode back to their camp and were safe.

Review Questions

1. Why did Will go to Robin's house?
2. Why did the sheriff arrest Will?
3. What did Robin pretend to do?

Robin Hood Meets Little John

Preview Questions

1. Who do you think Little John is?
2. Do you think he and Robin Hood will like each other?
3. What do you think the story in this chapter will be about?

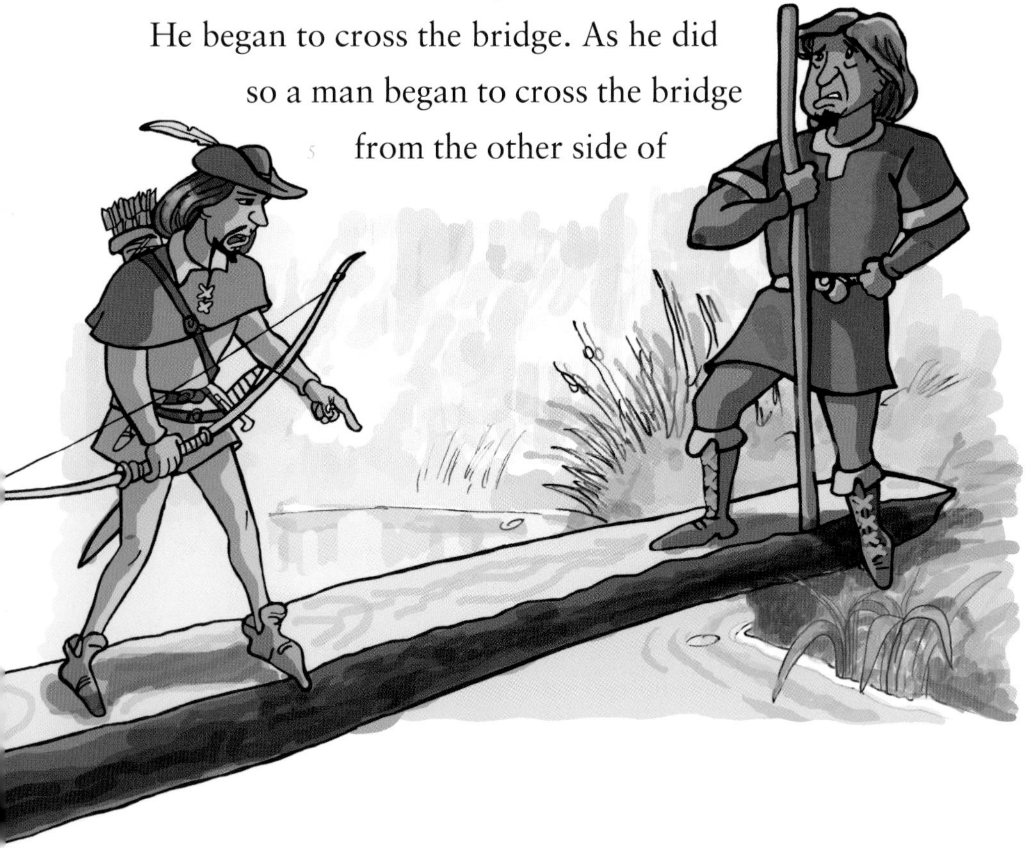

One day Robin went into the forest alone. He came to a bridge across a river. He began to cross the bridge. As he did so a man began to cross the bridge from the other side of the river. The two men met in the middle of the bridge There was not enough room for them to pass.

"I was on the bridge first," Robin said.

"You were not," the other man said. He was much taller than Robin. "I was on the bridge first."

Robin put an arrow in his **bow**.

"Move or I shall shoot you!" Robin demanded.

"Move or I shall hit you with my staff," the tall man said. He had a long, thick staff.

Robin laughed. "My arrow will kill you. Your staff won't kill me."

"You are a **coward** to fight me with a bow and arrow," the tall man said. "Fight me with a staff like mine."

"I am not a coward," Robin said. "I will fight you with a staff. Stay where you are."

Robin walked away to a tree. He cut a long, thick staff from the tree. He walked back to the middle of the bridge.

"Now I will fight you," he said. "We will find out who is stronger."

The two men fought for a long time. They hit one another hard with their staffs.

Then the tall man hit Robin very hard. He fell off the bridge and into the river.

"Now who is the stronger man?" the tall man shouted.

At this moment Will and some of Robin's men came out of the forest. Will saw Robin in the river.

"Shall we kill this man, Robin?" Will shouted.

"No," Robin answered as he climbed out of the river. "I want to talk to him."

"Who are you?" Robin asked the tall man. "What are you doing in the forest."

"I am looking for Robin Hood," the tall man said.

"Oh? Why are you looking for him?"

"I want to join his **band** of outlaws. I want to be one of his men."

"Why do you want to become an outlaw?" Robin asked him.

"I am already an outlaw," the tall man said. "Prince John took my lands and gave them to one of his men. Now I have no home."

Robin shook his hand. "Welcome. I am Robin Hood," he said. "I need strong and brave men like you. You may join my band of outlaws."

"What is your name?" Will asked him.

"John Little," the tall man said.

Robin laughed. "You are so tall," he said, "we will call you Little John!"

And this was how Little John became one of Robin's best friends.

Not long after Little John joined the band of outlaws, a **knight** rode through the forest. Robin saw him coming and said to Little John, "That knight looks sad. Ask him to join us for dinner. It is good to have a guest, sometimes."

Little John walked out of the trees and held up his hand.

"Stop, sir knight," he said. "My leader, Robin Hood, **invites** you to have dinner with us."

"I shall be pleased to," the knight said. "I heard about Robin Hood. He is a good man who takes from the rich and gives to the poor."

The knight followed Little John to the outlaws' camp.

"Welcome," Robin Hood said. "What is your name?"

"I am Sir Richard of Legh," the knight answered.

"Why do you look so sad?" Robin asked him.

"Tomorrow, I shall lose my lands. My wife and young children will have nowhere to live."

"Come and eat with us," Robin Hood said. "And

tell us your story."

Sir Richard joined the outlaws around their camp fire. As he ate, he told them his story.

"My eldest son left home to fight with King Richard. Soon after he left, I received some bad news. The enemy captured him. They asked for a **ransom** of one thousand pounds."

"That's a large **sum** of money," Little John said.

"Yes. And far more than I had, which was only six hundred pounds. I went to the **abbot** and asked him to lend me four hundred pounds. His **abbey** is very rich. It owns many farms, and the farmers all pay a high **rent**."

"And what did this rich abbot say?" Robin asked Sir Richard.

"He agreed to lend me the four hundred pounds. My son was returned to me, but if I do not repay the money tomorrow, the abbot will take all my lands. I need more time to save this amount of money.

"I pleaded with the abbot, but he just laughed and would not listen to me."

"The man is a **rogue!**" Little John shouted.

"How much money do you have?" Robin asked.

"Only a few pounds."

"Search him," Robin said.

Little John and Will searched the knight. They found only two pounds.

"The knight is telling the truth, Robin," Little John said.

"Then we shall lend him the money. Go to the shop, Will, and get four hundred pounds for this good knight."

"How can I thank you?" the knight asked.

"Come back to us in a year's time and repay the loan," Robin said. "I trust you."

The knight stayed with the outlaws that night and the next morning rode off to the abbey. The abbot was waiting for him.

"Do you have the money?" he demanded.

"I need more time," the knight answered.

"I have given you enough time! You agreed to give me your lands in exchange for the loan." The abbot smiled. He was a **greedy** and cruel man.

"Your abbey is rich," the knight said. "Why can't you give me more time to get the money?"

The abbot turned to some soldiers who were awaiting his orders.

"Go to this man's home," he commanded. "Make sure that his wife and children leave. Everything he owns is now mine!"

"Oh no, it isn't!" Sir Richard shouted. He took a bag of gold out of his pocket and threw it on the ground in front of the abbot.

Then he turned and went away. The abbot was very angry, but there was nothing he could do.

Review Questions

1. Why did Sir Richard of Legh borrow money from the abbot?
2. Why was Sir Richard sad?
3. Why couldn't the abbot have Sir Richard's lands?

CHAPTER 3

Robin Hood and the Quarrelsome Friar

Preview Questions

1. What is a friar?
2. Where do you think Robin Hood met the friar?
3. What do you think this story will be about?

One day Robin was walking in the forest. He came to a river. A **friar** was standing on the other side of the river. He lived alone in a small hut near the river. He had a small boat and ferried people across the river. He charged a few coins.

"I want to cross," Robin shouted at him. "Bring your boat over."

"What's the hurry?" the friar said. "And how do I know you have money to pay me?"

Robin held up his **purse.**

"Are you sure you really have the money?" the friar asked.

Robin became angry.

"Stop **arguing,** man," he said. "Do your job."

The friar got into his boat and rowed it across the river.

When he reached the other side, Robin got into the boat. The friar ferried him across the river. Before Robin could get out of the boat, the friar demanded, "Give me your purse."

"I will not," Robin said. "I told you I will pay you and I will."

"Then I must take your purse," the friar said. "I do not trust you."

He moved toward Robin. Quickly, Robin drew his sword. He held it at the friar's head.

"No man calls me a liar!" he shouted. "I must punish you, quarrelsome friar. You will now carry me back across the river on your back."

The friar was a huge man and very strong.

"Very well," he said, "if that is what you want, then you shall have it. Put away your sword and climb on to my back."

Robin put away his sword and climbed onto the friar's back. The river was shallow and the friar walked into it. He carried Robin to the middle of the river. There he bent down and **tipped** Robin into the river.

As Robin tried to stand up in the water, the friar took his sword from him.

"Now," he said. "It is my turn. You will carry me back."

At first Robin was angry, but then he began to laugh.

"I cannot be angry with you," he said. "Get on my back, good friar, and I will carry you to the river bank."

The friar agreed, and Robin began to carry him across the river.

Before they reached the river bank, however, Robin tipped the friar into the water.

Then he hurried to the river bank. He laughed as he watched the friar in the water.

"Now we are equal," he said.

"Oh no, we're not!" the friar shouted.

He ran out of the river and picked up a thick staff. Robin looked around and he also found a thick staff. The two men now began fighting with the staffs. They fought until they were exhausted. Then Robin said, "That's enough, good friar. Let's call it a **draw**."

The friar agreed, and the two men sat down on the river bank.

"Tell me who you are," Robin asked. "Tell me why you live alone in a small hut."

"I am Friar Tuck," the friar said. "I live alone but one day I shall find Robin Hood. Then I shall ask to

join him and live with him in Sherwood Forest."

"I am Robin Hood," Robin said. "And you are welcome to join our band. We need a holy man to join us in our prayers for King Richard's safe return."

"I will pray for that," Friar Tuck said. He held out his hand. "You will find me loyal and **trustworthy**, Robin."

"I know." The two men shook hands. Friar Tuck became a trusted member of Robin Hood's band of outlaws.

Review Questions

1. What did Robin want the friar to do?
2. Why was Robin angry with the friar?
3. What did Friar Tuck do after the fight?

Maid Marion Joins the Outlaws

Preview Questions

1. Who do you think Maid Marion is?
2. How do think they meet?
3. Why do you think Maid Marion will be important in the story of Robin Hood?

One day Sir Guy of Gisborne visited Marion's father, Lord Fitzwalter. Sir Guy was one of Prince John's men. He knew Lord Fitzwalter's daughter was in love with Robin Hood. He was hoping Maid Marion would lead him to Robin Hood.

Lord Fitzwalter had to welcome him. Then Sir Guy said, "I believe there is a fair in the village. Shall we go?"

"Let's do that," Lord Fitzwalter said. "There will be many sports to watch."

Sir Guy and Lord Fitzwalter rode to the village. There was a large crowd of people. They were watching an archery competition.

All of the competitors were men, except one.

"Who is that girl?" Sir Guy asked Lord Fitzwalter.

"Her name is Clorinda," Lord Fitzwalter answered. "She is a farmer's daughter."

Sir Guy did not believe him. He was sure the girl was Marion, Lord Fitzwalter's daughter.

"She will lead me to Robin Hood," he thought. "Everyone knows they want to marry."

Clorinda shot her arrow, and it hit the target. The crowd cheered. Then a man dressed in green walked up to her.

"I will try to do better than that," he said.

He shot an arrow. It hit the target close to Clorinda's arrow.

"Who is that man?" Sir Guy asked Lord Fitzwalter.

"I don't know," Lord Fitzwalter lied. He knew the man was Robin Hood.

"Well, I know who he is," Sir Guy said. "He is Robin Hood. And I am here to **arrest** him."

"You and who else?" Lord Fitzwalter said. "How many men in green do you see?"

Sir Guy looked at the crowd. He saw many men in green.

"They are all Robin Hood's men," Lord Fitzwalter said. "You will need help to arrest him, but I have no men here to help you."

"Then I shall ride to Nottingham and get the sheriff. He will come with his men, and we will arrest Robin Hood. He is an outlaw, and Prince John wants him in prison."

Sir Guy rode off to Nottingham.

He soon returned with the sheriff and his men.

"Where is Robin Hood?" he asked everyone.

"We don't know," was the reply.

The sheriff said, "He's gone back into the forest. He can't have gone far. We'll catch him."

Sir Guy, the sheriff and his men rode into the forest. They soon came to a river.

There was a **narrow** bridge across the river. Friar Tuck was standing in the middle of the bridge.

"Get out of the way, friar," the sheriff demanded.

"You get out of my way," Friar Tuck answered back.

"We are on Prince John's business," the sheriff said. "Get out of the way, or it will be bad for you."

Friar Tuck laughed. He swung his large staff and hit the sheriff. He fell off his horse into the river.

"Arrest that man!" the sheriff shouted.

His men ran forward, but Friar Tuck used his thick staff to beat them off. He knocked several of them into the water. Then Robin Hood and his men came out of the trees. They had bows and arrows. Sir Guy, the sheriff, and his men only had swords.

Robins' **archers** easily beat them. Sir Guy was wounded and so was the sheriff. They rode back to Nottingham.

The next day the sheriff sent some of his men to Lord Fitzwalter's castle.

"We know that your daughter, Marion, pretended to be Clorinda," the leader of the men said. "We know that she is a friend of the outlaw Robin Hood. In the name of Prince John, she must take us to him."

"How do I know that you are not outlaws in

disguise?" Lord Fitzwalter asked. "And you are talking nonsense. My daughter is not Clorinda. If you are not outlaws, then tell Prince John to come here himself."

The sheriff's men argued, but there was nothing they could do. Lord Fitzwalter had many archers **guarding** his castle.

"We shall come again," the leader of the sheriff's men said. Then he and the other soldiers went away.

Lord Fitzwalter went to his daughter's room.

"You must hide somewhere in the castle," he told his daughter.

"No, father," Marion said. "Those men will come back with Prince John. He will search the castle and find me. Then he will make me take him to Robin. I must go to him now and stay with him in the forest. He and his men will protect me."

"You cannot stay with Robin Hood," her father said. "You are not married to him. And I will not allow you to marry an outlaw."

"I shall not stay with him as his wife," Marion said. "I will be one of his men. You know that he is really a good man, Father. He is an outlaw only because Prince

John took his lands. When King Richard returns from the war, he will give Robin back his lands."

Marion put on a man's clothes and left the castle. She carried a sword and her bow and arrows. She walked into the forest. She walked all day and then as the sun began to set, Robin Hood came out of the trees.

"Who are you and where are you going?" Robin demanded.

"That is none of your business," Marion said.

"You will answer my question," Robin Hood demanded, "or I shall cut you in two."

Marion put down her bow and arrow and drew her sword. For several minutes she fought Robin until he said, "Enough. You are as good with a sword as me. I do not wish to hurt you. But tell me who you are and what you are doing in Sherwood Forest."

Marion took off her hat. Robin saw her long hair.

"Don't you recognize me, Robin?" she asked.

Now Robin knew who the young man really was.

"Oh, Marion," he said, putting his arms around her. "I nearly wounded you."

Marion laughed. "And I nearly wounded you. But

all is well, and you know that I can fight as well as you can."

Robin and Marion went back to his camp together. The outlaws had a great **feast** that night.

Review Questions

1. Why did Sir Guy go into the forest with his men?
2. Why didn't Robin recognize Marion when he was fighting her?
3. In what way was Marion as good as Robin?

CHAPTER 5

Robin and the Silver Arrow

Preview Questions

1. Have you seen an arrow before?
2. What do you think is special about a silver arrow?
3. What do you think Prince John will try to do to find Robin Hood?

The people of Nottingham hated Prince John. He was cruel and greedy. He took their lands and gave them to his friends and followers. He put many people in prison.

"I know I am not popular," he said to Sir Guy. Sir Guy was a **wicked** knight who wanted to put Robin Hood in prison. He wanted Maid Marion for his wife.

"There is a way to make you popular," Sir Guy said. "Hold an archery **competition**, and give a silver **arrow** as a prize. Archers from everywhere will want to compete. There will be a huge crowd of people to watch them."

He thought to himself, "Robin Hood will want to compete. Then I can arrest him."

"That's a good idea, Sir Guy," Prince John said. "Send men to every village and town in Nottingham. They must tell everyone about the competition."

Robin Hood heard about the competition.

"I must compete," he said to Little John and Will Scarlet. "I am one of the best archers in the country. It will please me very much to win the prince's silver arrow."

"It will be dangerous, Robin," Little John said. "Prince John, Sir Guy, and the sheriff will expect you to compete. They will be looking for you."

"I know," Robin said. "I will go in disguise."

"We will come with you," Will Scarlet said.

"No. I must go alone," Robin said. "It is too dangerous for more than one of us to go."

"If we cannot be with you," Little John said, "then all of us will wait for you just outside town. If you get into trouble, we shall be there to help you."

When the day of competition arrived, Robin put a hood over his head and rode into Nottingham. When he arrived, there were crowds of people waiting for the competition to begin. Prince John was sitting on a stage. Sir Guy and the Sheriff of Nottingham were sitting with him. Prince John's soldiers were everywhere.

There were many competitors, and they shot arrows at

a target throughout the day. By the end of the afternoon, only three archers were left in the competition. There was an archer from Delaware, one from Wirral, and Robin Hood from Sherwood.

"One of you will win the silver arrow," Prince John said.

A new target was put up. In the center of the target was a black circle.

The archers had to shoot an arrow in the circle.

"The archer whose arrow is nearest to the center of the circle will be the winner," Prince John announced.

The archer from Delaware shot first.

He drew back his bow. There was silence from the crowd. The archer let the arrow go, and it flew straight at the target. It hit the target just outside the edge of the black circle.

The archer from Wirral shot next. The crowd was even quieter. "Could he get an arrow inside the black circle?" the crowd wondered.

He drew back his bow. The archer let the arrow go, and it flew straight at the target. It hit the target just inside the black circle.

Now it was the archer from Sherwood's turn.

He drew back his bow. The archer let it go, and the arrow flew straight toward its target and hit the center of the black circle.

The crowd cheered.

"The archer from Sherwood is the winner," Prince John said. "Come forward and **collect** your prize."

Robin Hood walked to the stage. He knelt in front of Prince John.

"Take off your hood in front of the prince," Sir Guy said.

Before Robin could say anything, the sheriff pulled the hood off his head.

"It's Robin Hood, the outlaw!" Sir Guy shouted. "Arrest him!"

The soldiers ran forward. Robin moved away. He drew his bow and fired arrows at the soldiers. Then his men ran to help him. Soon there were more than twenty archers shooting arrows at the soldiers as they ran out of town.

"Where can we go?" Little John shouted to Robin. "There will be soldiers on horses after us soon."

"We must find a friend who will hide us," Robin said. "There will be one somewhere in Sherwood Forest."

It got dark very soon.

"It will not be easy for the soldiers to catch us now," Robin said.

They ran through the forest, getting as far from Nottingham as possible.

Little John saw a light ahead. "Look, Robin," he shouted. "There's a light. Perhaps we will find a friend there to hide us."

They ran toward the light and came to a castle.

Robin **knocked** on the castle door.

"Who is there?" a **watchman** shouted from inside.

"Robin of Sherwood Forest and his men. We ask for **shelter** for the night."

"Wait. I will speak to my master," the watchman answered.

"Whose castle is this?" Robin asked.

"It is the home Sir Richard of Legh," the watchman said.

"Then tell him it is Robin Hood who asks for shelter," Robin said. He turned to Little John and said, "This must be the Sir Richard to whom we lent the money. We shall be safe here."

Soon the watchman opened the gate of the castle. Sir Richard came out to meet Robin.

"Welcome to my home, Robin," he said. "I am so pleased to see you."

"Sir Guy and the sheriff are after us," Robin said. "Can you hide us?"

"I shall be pleased to," Sir Richard answered.

He took Robin and his men to a hiding place beneath his castle.

"Stay here," he said. "Sir Guy will never find you here. I will send food and drink to you."

Robin and his men stayed in the castle all night. The next morning Sir Guy, the sheriff, and their men came to the castle.

"We are looking for Robin Hood," Sir Guy said.

"You are looking in the wrong place," Sir Richard told him.

"Are you sure Robin Hood did not come here during the night?" the sheriff asked.

"Do you dare to call me a liar?" Sir Richard demanded.

Both Sir Guy and the sheriff believed Robin was in the castle, but there was nothing they could do. They could not go into Sir Richard's castle without his permission. Only the king or Prince John could do that.

"Prince John will be angry," Sir Guy said.

"Where is the Prince?" Sir Richard asked.

"He is in London," Sir Guy answered. Then he left with the sheriff and his men.

Later, Sir Richard told Robin, "You will be safe here

for a few days, but Prince John may come back. Then I must let him come into my castle."

"We will soon leave," Robin answered.

And the next day they left the castle and returned to their camp in the forest.

Review Questions

1. What was Robin's disguise?
2. How did Sir Guy know that the winner of the competition was Robin Hood?
3. Where did Robin stay after the competition?

Robin Becomes a Butcher for a Day

Preview Questions

1. What is a butcher?
2. Is there a butcher in your neighborhood?
3. What do you think this chapter will be about?

One day Robin said to Little John, "I am a little bored, friend. What can we do for fun?"

"The **butcher** of Nottingham will pass by soon. He'll have a **cart** full of meat."

"Is he a good man?" Robin asked Little John.

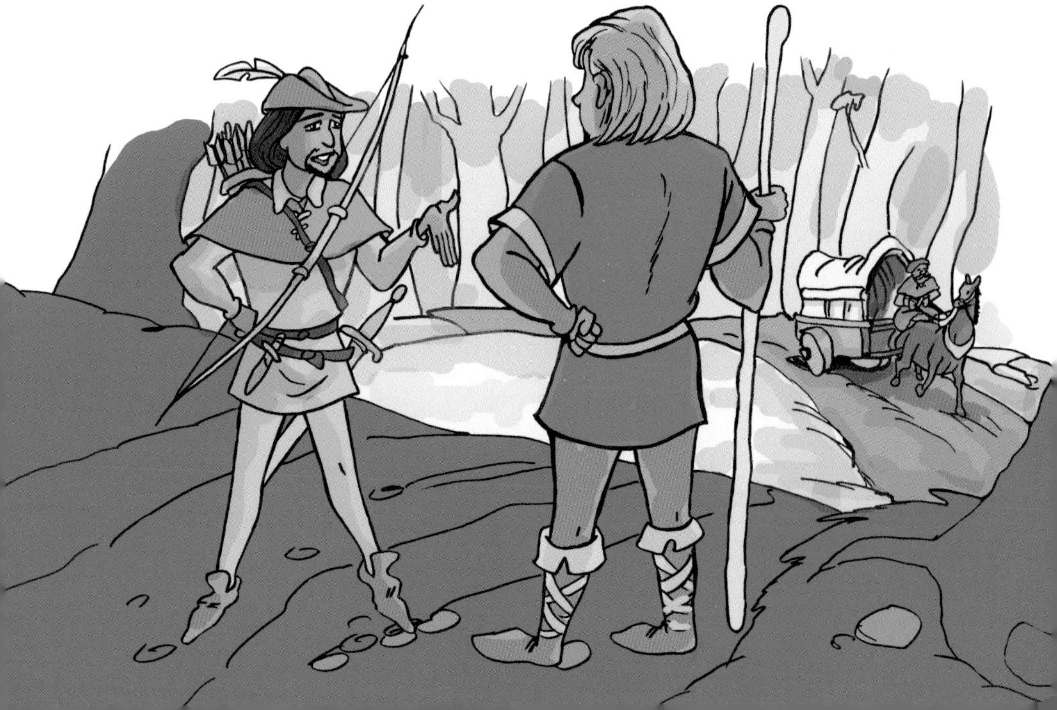

"He is a strong man and can fight with a staff," Little John answered.

"Then I shall fight him for his cart full of meat," Robin said.

He walked out of the forest into the road and held up his hand.

"Good day, butcher," he said. "It is time to give me and my men some meat."

The butcher got down from his cart. He had a large staff in his hand.

"You will have to fight me for it," he said.

Quickly, Robin cut a staff from a nearby tree.

"That I will gladly do," he said.

The two men fought for many minutes. At last, the butcher said, "No more. I cannot fight any more. I am older than you, Robin Hood."

"Then let me have your cart full of meat. Stay in Sherwood with Little John and my men until I return."

Robin put on a disguise and got on the butcher's horse. He rode all day until he reached Nottingham. There he pulled the cart to the market place.

"Good meat for sale," he shouted. "Good cheap meat for sale!"

Soon there were many women buying the meat. It was so cheap that they bought as much as they could. When there was only a little left, Robin said, "I must take this to the sheriff's wife. She must have her share."

Robin took the rest of the meat to the sheriff's house. Robin knocked on the door and the sheriff's wife answered the door.

"This is for you," Robin said. "It is only right that the sheriff's wife should have her share."

The sheriff's wife was very pleased by this.

"Thank you, good butcher," she said. "Please stay with us for the night. Join us for our meal of your good meat."

And so Robin ate dinner that night with the sheriff, his family and friends.

"What news is there of King Richard?" Robin asked the sheriff.

"It is not good news," the sheriff said. "He is a **prisoner** of the enemy."

"Prince John will pay a ransom for him, won't he?" Robin said.

"Many people think he will not," one of the sheriff's friends said. "Prince John wants to be king. He doesn't care if his brother dies in prison."

"What do the people think?" Robin asked.

"The rich want Prince John to be king," another of the friends said. "The poor want King Richard to come home safely."

Robin was careful not to say anything. He did not want the sheriff to know that he hated Prince John.

"I am tired," he said. "Tomorrow will be a long day. I must go to a friend's farm. He will sell me a hundred bulls, also called 'steers,' at a low price."

The sheriff asked, "Will he sell me steers for a cheap price?"

"I'm sure that he will," Robin said. "Come to his farm with me. Bring **plenty** of money with you."

The next day, Robin left Nottingham with the sheriff and his men. Soon they were in Sherwood Forest.

"Is the farm much farther?" the sheriff asked. He did not like being deep in the forest. He knew that Robin Hood and the outlaws were there.

"It's not much farther," Robin answered.

They continued riding deeper into the forest.

"Where are these steers?" the sheriff asked. "I do not want to go farther into the forest."

"You will soon see them."

Robin took out his horn and blew it. Immediately, hundreds of red deer came out of the trees.

"These are not steers," the sheriff said. "They are deer. They belong to the king. All the deer in the land belong to the king."

"The king's men have to eat," Robin said.

He blew his horn again. This time Little John, Friar Tuck, Maid Marion, and many of the outlaws came out of the trees. Robin took off his disguise.

The sheriff was very angry. "One day I will arrest you," he said. "You will be hanged as a thief."

The outlaws quickly took the sheriff's money and all of his men's swords. Then Robin said, "Go back to Nottingham, Sheriff. Tell Prince John to pay the ransom for our good king. If he does not, we will take the money from the rich and pay the ransom ourselves."

The sheriff and his men rode back to Nottingham. Robin and his men went back to their **camp**. The butcher was waiting for them. Robin told him the news about the king. The butcher said, "You and your men like to eat meat. You need a good butcher. I do not have a wife or family. Let me join you."

"You are welcome," Robin said. "We need men who can fight as well as you can and who can butcher a deer for us when we are hungry."

Review Questions

1. Why did the sheriff's wife ask Robin to stay the night?
2. What did the sheriff want to buy?
3. Why was the sheriff angry?

Robin Hood and the Tanner

Preview Questions

1. What do you think a tanner does?
2. Are there any tanners in your neighborhood?
3. What do you think this story will be about?

"Who is that man riding toward us?" Robin asked to one of his men as they sat on the roadside.

"I do not know, Robin," the man said. "But I can smell him from here."

"Then he is a **tanner,**" Robin said. "Tanners make

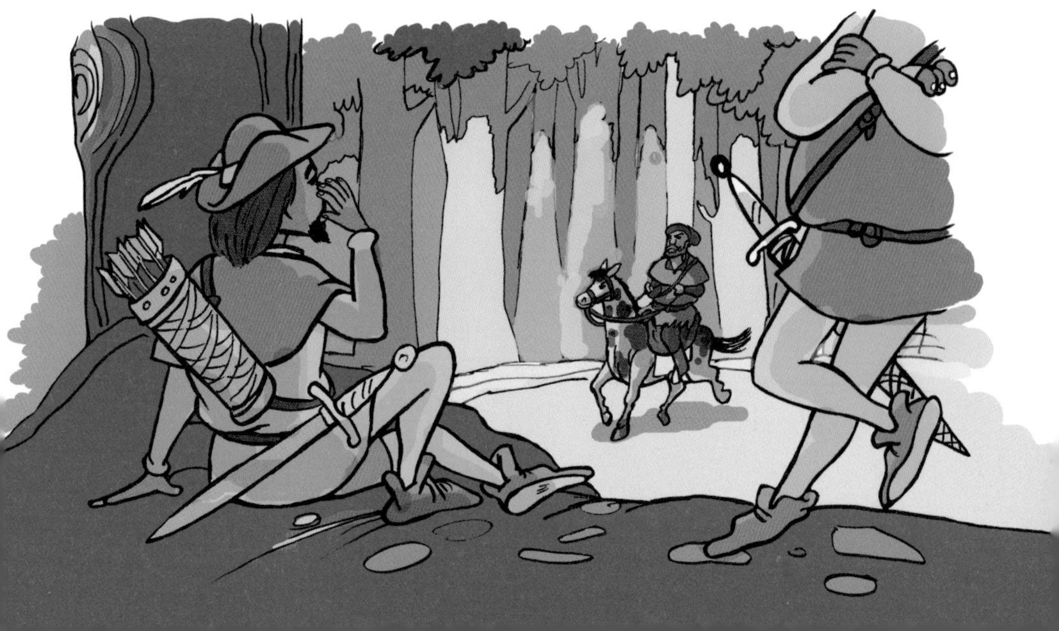

their money from turning the **hides** of animals into good leather. It is smelly work."

Robin stood up and held up his hand.

"Good day to you," he said to the tanner. "Where are you going?"

The tanner got down from his horse.

"I am looking for Robin Hood," he said.

"Oh? And why are you looking for that outlaw?" Robin asked him.

The tanner handed Robin a piece of paper. Robin read what was on it.

"I will give five hundred pounds
to any man who brings me Robin

Hood, alive or dead. Signed, *The Sheriff of Nottingham.*"

"That's a lot of money," Robin said. "Why is the sheriff so angry with this outlaw?"

"Robin Hood pretended to be a butcher and tricked him," the tanner said. "He took his money and the swords of his men."

"A very bad thing to do," Robin said, trying not to laugh. "But why do you want to find Robin Hood? Has he made you angry?"

"No," the tanner said, "I want the five hundred pounds. Tanning is smelly work. With five hundred pounds, I can have a different business."

Robin said, "What will you give me if I take you to Robin Hood?"

"Will he be alone?" the tanner asked.

"He will be alone," Robin said. "He will not have any outlaws with him."

"Then I will give you one hundred of the five hundred."

"Very well," Robin said. "I will take you to him tomorrow. Now it is late. Let us find an inn for the night and eat and drink."

Robin and the tanner, whose name was Arthur, soon

found an inn. Robin spoke secretly to the innkeeper.

"This man wants to find Robin Hood," he said, "and take him to the sheriff. I want him to drink too much so that he will fall asleep."

The innkeeper was a good friend of Robin and he said, "I will give him the strongest drink I have."

Robin and Arthur ate and drank for more than an hour. Then Arthur fell asleep.

Robin tried to wake him, but he could not.

"That is a very strong drink, innkeeper," he said. "Let me now see how much money this tanner has."

Robin looked in the tanner's purse. There were only a few coins and the letter from the sheriff.

"I'll take the letter," he said to the innkeeper. "He can pay you with the coins when he wakes up in the morning."

Robin stayed the night in the inn and the next morning set off on the road toward his camp.

The tanner woke up soon after Robin left.

"Your friend has gone," the innkeeper said. "He took the letter from the sheriff. Now you must pay me for the food and drink."

"Did he not pay his share?"

The innkeeper laughed.

"Robin Hood owes nothing to a man hoping to arrest him," he said.

"Robin Hood! Are you saying that man was Robin Hood?"

"It was. And he made a fool of you. Now pay for the food and drink."

The tanner gave the innkeeper all his coins. Then he got on his horse and rode after Robin.

Soon he saw Robin walking along the road. He got off his horse and drew his sword.

With a laugh Robin said, "Do you have the hundred pounds you promised me?"

"I'll cut you down before I pay you even one coin," the tanner said. He moved toward Robin.

Robin held up his hand.

"I have no sword," he said. "Are you the kind of man to fight a man without a sword? I do not think so. We ate and drank together. That is what friends do. If you want to arrest me, then fight me fairly. Cut yourself a staff. I will do the same."

"Very well," the tanner said. "I will fight you fairly. Then I will take you to the sheriff."

The two men cut staffs from nearby trees. They fought one another for more than two hours. Both their heads became bloody.

"Let us not fight any more," Robin said. "If we continue, we shall both die from our wounds."

"I must arrest you," the tanner said. "I must have that five hundred pounds. I cannot pay you the hundred I owe you without that money."

"You are a most honest man," Robin said. "You are the kind of man I want. Join me and my men in Sherwood Forest. You can earn far more than five hundred pounds as an outlaw with us." He laughed. "Then you can pay me the hundred you owe me."

At this moment, Little John walked out of the trees toward them. When he saw the tanner, he smiled and shouted, "Cousin, is it really you?"

He ran up to the tanner and took his hand.

"This is my cousin, Arthur," he told Robin. "We were good friends when we were young."

"And we shall be good friends again," the tanner said. "I am going to live with you in Sherwood Forest and become one of Robin Hood's men."

And this he did. The two cousins became two of Robin's most trusted men.

Review Questions

1. What did Robin Hood pretend to do?
2. Why did Robin and the tanner fight?
3. Why did the tanner join the outlaws?

The Death of Robin Hood

Preview Questions

1. How long do you think Robin Hood lived in the forest?
2. How do you think Robin Hood died?
3. What do you think happened to all the other outlaws?

For many years, Robin Hood and his men had adventures. They robbed the rich and gave to the poor. They fought the sheriff's men. Robin waited patiently for King Richard to return from the wars. "Then and only then will I get my lands back and stop being an outlaw," he told his men. "Until that time we will live in Sherwood Forest."

More and more men and women joined the outlaws in Sherwood Forest. Prince John became very angry.

"I will give one thousand pounds for the head of Robin Hood," he told the Sheriff of Nottingham.

"I will need more men to catch Robin Hood," the sheriff thought. "I must borrow money to pay them."

The sheriff borrowed money from rich merchants. Soon he had more men than Robin Hood.

"I must win those thousand pounds," the sheriff told his wife. "If I do not, we shall lose everything."

When his army was ready, the sheriff left Nottingham for Sherwood Forest. Before they reached Robin's camp, one of his men saw them. He blew his horn three times.

Robin said, "The sheriff and his men are coming. We know he has a large army now. This will be the greatest battle of our lives. We must win this battle to stay free."

Robin and the outlaws fought a great battle against the sheriff and his men. Many men were

killed and wounded on both sides. There were too many of the sheriff's men for the outlaws to beat. At last, the sheriff's men captured Robin and took him to the prison in Nottingham. They tied him with rope and put him in a **cell**. The cell was at the top of a tall tower.

During the night, Robin was able to untie the rope. There was a small window in the tower. Robin tied one end of the rope to a ring in the wall of his cell. He tied the other end to himself. Then he climbed through the window. The cell was a long way from the ground. Slowly, Robin climbed down the rope. He was halfway

down when the rope broke. Robin fell to the ground. He lay there for a long time. His leg hurt badly.

Before morning, Robin was able to stand up. Then he limped away from the tower.

"The sheriff's men will soon go to the cell to give me food," he thought, "They will see that I am not in the cell. I must get as far away from here as I can."

Robin traveled all day and all night. The pain in his leg was very bad.

"I cannot go on much farther," he thought. "I must find somewhere safe to hide and rest."

That evening, he came to a small fishing village. The sheriff's men were not far behind him. He knocked on the door of a small **cottage**. An old woman opened the door.

"Good woman," Robin said. "Robbers are after me. They will kill me if they catch me. Let me hide and rest here."

The old woman looked at Robin.

"He has a kind face," she thought. "And he is hurt."

"You may stay here for a few days," she said.

Robin stayed with the old woman for many days. Slowly, he got a little better, and he was able to walk again.

"How can I pay you?" he said to the old woman. "I have no money."

"I own a fishing boat," the old woman said. "You can work with the fishermen. They go to sea tonight."

Robin joined the fishermen on the boat. He worked as hard as he could, but he did not know how to fish. He did not catch anything.

"You are useless," the captain of the boat said. "We will not share anything with you."

At that moment, one of the fisherman shouted, "Boat to the east! A **pirate** ship. We will all be killed!"

Robin said, "I am not a good fisherman, but I can use a bow. Lend me your bow and as many arrows as you have."

The captain of the boat said, "If you fight as well as you fish, we will all die."

"Trust me," Robin said.

The captain of the fishing boat gave Robin his bow and all the arrows on the ship.

The pirate ship came nearer and nearer. Robin took aim. He shot the first arrow. It killed the pirate captain. Robin shot arrow after arrow. Soon all the pirates were dead.

"There will be gold on the pirate ship," the captain said. "You will have half of it, Robin."

"I don't want the gold. Give half of it to the old woman who owns this boat and build homes for the poor with the other half. Now take me back to the shore."

Robin knew it was time to go home. His leg was hurting again. "I am very ill," he said to the captain. "I want to be with my men."

Robin left the fishermen and set off for Sherwood Forest.

* * *

After the battle with the sheriff's men, Maid Marion waited for Robin to return. Days and weeks passed,

but he did not come.

Sir Guy came to see her.

"Robin Hood is dead," he said. "Now you can marry me."

"I will never marry you," Maid Marion said. "I will become a **nun**."

She left Sherwood Forest and went to a nunnery.

"I want to stay here and become a nun," she told the **Abbess**.

"You are welcome," the Abbess said, and she gave Maid Marion nun's clothes.

Maid Marion worked in the gardens of the nunnery.

Soon after Marion came to the nunnery, Robin Hood knocked on the door. The Abbess opened it.

"What do you want?" she asked.

Robin said, "Good mother, I am very sick. I must rest or I will die. Please let me stay the night."

The Abbess knew who Robin was. "I will help Prince John catch this outlaw," she thought. "Then he will give money to the nunnery. We will all be able to have a better life. We will have better food and better clothes."

She said, "You may stay a few nights. I will try to make you better."

"I am looking for my friend Maid Marion," Robin said. "Do you know where she is?"

"She is not here," the Abbess said. "There are only nuns here."

She took Robin to a small room. He lay down.

"You have too much blood," the Abbess said. "I must take some away."

She made a cut in Robin's arm. The blood flowed into a bowl.

"That is better," the Abbess said. She tied a tight cloth around Robin's arm.

"Now sleep. You will be stronger in the morning."

The Abbess left Robin. She locked Maid Marion in her room.

"She must now know that Robin Hood is alive and

that he is here," she thought.

Robin was very tired. He slept deeply. While he slept, the Abbess untied the cloth around his arm. Robin's blood began to flow again. When he awoke, he was very weak.

"That Abbess is trying to kill me," he thought. "I must get away from here."

He was very weak, but he left the nunnery and walked until he came to the forest. He went into the forest and lay down. He could not walk any farther. He took out his horn and blew on it. Soon Little John and some of his men came out of the forest.

"We thought you were dead, Robin," Little John said. "Maid Marion is a nun now."

"I am dying, Little John," Robin said.

"No, Robin!" Little John said. "Friar Tuck will help you get better."

"No one can help me now," Robin said. "It is too late. Look at my leg."

Little John looked at Robin's leg.

"Oh, Robin," he said. "Your leg is black and green."

"It is full of **poison**," Robin said, "and the poison is now flowing through my body. Give me your bow and an arrow. Bury me where the arrow falls."

Little John handed Robin his bow and an arrow. Robin shot his last arrow.

"Goodbye, good friend," Robin said. "Say goodbye to all my trusted men."

Then he died.

Little John and Robin's men buried him where the arrow fell.

When Maid Marion heard of Robin's death, she went to another nunnery. There she soon became the Abbess. She spent the rest of her life helping the poor.

Review Questions

1. How did Robin escape from the tower?
2. How did Robin help the fishermen?
3. Why did Robin die?

NEW WORDS

Chapter 1

outlaw *n.* a person who is running away from the police

afraid *adj.* scared; full of fear

shout *v.* to speak very loudly

sheriff *n.* a police officer

jewel *n.* a stone worth a lot of money

quarrel *v.* to talk very loudly with a person because you are angry

search *v.* to look for someone or something

prison *n.* a place where criminals are kept

beggar *n.* a person who asks for money

gallows *n.* a device for killing people

hangman *n.* a person who kills by hanging people with a rope

Chapter 2

bow *n.* a stick tied at both ends with a string

coward *n.* a person who is not brave; a person who is afraid to fight

band *n.* a group of people who work together

knight *n.* a soldier from long ago who rode horses

invite *v.* to ask someone to come to your house

ransom *n.* the money given to get a person out of captivity

sum *n.* an amount of money

abbot *n.* a man in charge of monks

abbey *n.* a place where monks or nuns live

rent *n.* the money you pay to live somewhere

rogue *n.* a robber; a crook

greedy *adj.* money-hungry

Chapter 3

friar *n.* a man in a religious group

purse *n.* a small bag for carrying money

argue *v.* to try to get someone to agree with you

tip *v.* to push someone down

draw *v.* to pull out

trustworthy *adj.* honest

Chapter 4

arrest *v.* to have the police take you away

narrow *adj.* thin; not wide

archer *n.* a person who uses a bow and arrow

disguise *v.* to change the way you look

guard *v.* to watch someone

feast *n.* a very large meal; many different types of food to eat

Chapter 5

wicked *adj.* being a bad person

competition *n.* an event where people try to win a prize

arrow *n.* a straight stick with a sharp point

collect *v.* to get something

knock *v.* to hit a door with your fist

watchman *n.* a person who protects a place

shelter *n.* a place to hide from weather or people

Chapter 6

butcher *n.* a person who sells meat

cart *n.* a vehicle pulled by a horse

prisoner *n.* a person kept against their will

plenty *n.* a large amount of something

camp *n.* an outdoor shelter for many people

Chapter 7

tanner *n.* a person who turns animal skins into leather

hide *n.* the skin of an animal

Chapter 8

cell *n.* a very small room

cottage *n.* a very small house

pirate *n.* a person who robs others at sea

nun *n.* a very religious woman who lives in a convent

abbess *n.* a woman in charge of nuns

poison *n.* material that will kill you if it gets into your body

The Death of Robin Hood

Cast

Marion
Little John
Friar Tuck
Will
1st Man
Woman
2nd Man
Abbess
Robin

In the outlaws' camp in Sherwood Forest, Maid Marion is talking to Little John, Friar Tuck, and Will Scarlet.

Marion: Robin left three weeks ago. Where can he be?

Little John: Don't worry, Marion. He will be safe somewhere.

Friar Tuck: He can look after himself.

Will: He has many friends. I am sure he is staying with someone.

Marion: I don't think so. Why isn't there a message from him?

Little John: Perhaps he sent a message but the sheriff's men arrested the messenger.

Friar Tuck: I will go into the town and ask questions.

Little John: No. It is too dangerous. The sheriff's men are everywhere.

Marion: We must do something. If Robin is in prison, we must help him to escape.

Will: I will go into town. I will disguise myself as a woman. Lend me some of your clothes, Marion.

Little John: If the sheriff catches you, he will hang you.

Will: He won't catch me.

Marion: Take great care, Will.

Will: I will.

In Nottingham, Will, disguised as a woman, is asking about Robin.

Will: Excuse me, are there any prisoners in the tower?

1st Man: Why do you ask?

Will: I am looking for my brother.

1st Man: What did he do wrong?

Will: He said bad things about Prince John.

1st Man: The tower is full of men who have said bad things about Prince John.

Will: I'm sure. Do you know the names of any of them?

1st Man: No. I never ask questions. I don't want to be locked in the tower. And if you don't want to be arrested, don't ask questions.

Will: Thank you.

Will goes into an inn. He speaks to the innkeeper's wife.

Will: A glass of your best ale, good woman.

Woman: Have you money to pay for it?

Will: Here. I am not a beggar.

Woman: You look like one in those old clothes.

Will: I am looking for my brother. Who is in the tower now?

Woman: Do you think that your brother is in the tower?

Will: Perhaps. He is a foolish man. He cannot keep his mouth shut.

Woman: Many men are hanged for that. Robin Hood was in the tower, but he escaped. Just in time. The sheriff wanted to hang him.

Will: Robin Hood? Who is that?

Woman: What? You don't know who Robin Hood is?

Will: No.

Woman: He is an outlaw. He lives in Sherwood Forest with other outlaws.

Will: Why is he an outlaw?

Woman: Prince John took his lands. That's all I will say.

Will: When did Robin Hood escape from the tower?

Woman: Two days ago.

2nd Man: You're wrong, woman. Robin Hood died trying to escape. He fell from a window in the tower. He was climbing down a rope. It broke.

Will: Are you sure that he is dead?

2nd Man: No man could live after a fall like that.

Will: Where is he buried?

2nd Man: You'll have to ask the sheriff.

Will returns to the camp in Sherwood Forest.

Marion: Do you have any news, Will?

Will: Yes. But it's not good news, Marion.

Little John: Where is Robin?

Will: I believe he is dead.

Marion: Dead! How do you know?

Will: He was in the tower. He escaped by climbing out of the window. Sadly, he fell to the ground.

Marion: Where is he buried?

Will: I don't know.

Friar Tuck: I cannot believe that Robin is dead.

Will: I'm afraid he is. I looked at the tower. If Robin fell from the top he cannot be alive.

Little John: What can we do?

Will: There is nothing we can do. You must be the new leader, Little John.

Little John: No. Maid Marion must be our leader.

Marion: I will not lead you. Without Robin, my life is nothing. I shall go to a nunnery and spend the rest of my life in prayer.

In the nunnery, the Abbess is making a cut in Robin's arm.

Abbess: You have too much blood. You will not get better unless you lose some. How did you hurt your leg?

Robin: I was fishing. A pirate ship attacked our boat. We fought them off, but one of them cut me with his sword.

Abbess: That does not look like a sword wound. It is a broken bone.

Robin: I fell.

Abbess: Who are you?

Robin: A fisherman.

Abbess: You do not speak like a fisherman. But rest now. You will be better in the morning.

Marion goes to the nunnery. She speaks to the Abbess.

Marion: Mother, I wish to become a nun.

Abbess: Why is that, my child?

Marion: My very good friend is dead. I do not want to live in the outside world.

Abbess: Who was your friend?

Marion: Robin Hood.

Abbess: That outlaw!

Marion: He was an outlaw because Prince John took his lands. Robin was a good and kind man.

Abbess: You may stay here and pray.

Robin is walking into the forest. He is very weak. He falls to the ground. He blows his horn. Little John and Friar Tuck run out of the forest.

Little John: Robin! What is the matter?

Robin: I am dying, Little John.

Friar Tuck: No. You are just tired.

Little John: Look at his leg, Friar Tuck.

Friar Tuck looks at Robin's leg.

Friar Tuck: It is not good. It is turning black and green.

Robin: I know, and the poison is flowing through my body.

Little John: Can you do something for him, Friar Tuck?

Friar Tuck: I have some medicine.

Robin: It is too late, and I am too weak. Lend me your bow and an arrow, Little John.

Little John: What for?

Robin: I shall shoot one last arrow. Bury me where it falls.

Robin shoots an arrow. Then he lies back and dies.

Little John: He was a good man.

Friar Tuck: Who will be our leader now?

Little John: Maid Marion.

Friar Tuck: I do not think so. She will stay in a nunnery. She will not want to leave it now that Robin is dead. Little John, you will have to lead us.

COMPASS CLASSIC READERS Series

LEVEL 1

- **The Emperor's New Clothes** by Hans Christian Andersen
- **Black Beauty** by Anna Sewell
- **Grimm's Fairy Tales** by Jacob and Wilhelm Grimm
- **Favorite Asian Folk Tales** by Various Authors
- **The Wind in the Willows** by Kenneth Grahame
- **Doctor Dolittle** by Hugh Lofting
- **Just So Stories** by Rudyard Kipling
- **The Jungle Book** by Rudyard Kipling
- **Aesop's Fables** by Aesop
- **The Happy Prince** by Oscar Wilde

LEVEL 2

- **The Arabian Nights** by Various Authors
- **Robin Hood** by Howard Pyle
- **Alice in Wonderland** by Lewis Carroll
- **The Wizard of Oz** by L. Frank Baum
- **The Railway Children** by Edith Nesbit
- **The Secret Garden** by Frances Hodgson Burnett
- **White Fang** by Jack London
- **The Adventures of Tom Sawyer** by Mark Twain
- **Peter Pan** by J.M. Barrie
- **Anne of Green Gables** by Lucy Maud Montgomery

LEVEL 3

- **The Merchant of Venice** by William Shakespeare
- **Treasure Island** by Robert Louis Stevenson
- **King Solomon's Mines** by Henry Rider Haggard
- **The Time Machine** by H.G. Wells
- **Robinson Crusoe** by Daniel Defoe
- **Romeo and Juliet** by William Shakespeare
- **Dr. Jekyll and Mr. Hyde** by Robert Louis Stevenson
- **Frankenstein** by Mary Shelley
- **A Christmas Carol** by Charles Dickens
- **20,000 Leagues Under the Sea** by Jules Verne

LEVEL 4

- **David Copperfield** by Charles Dickens
- **The Thirty-Nine Steps** by John Buchan
- **Oliver Twist** by Charles Dickens
- **Little Women** by Louisa May Alcott
- **Sherlock Holmes** by Sir Arthur Conan Doyle
- **Tales of Mystery & Imagination** by Ed
- **Around the World in Eighty Day**
- **The Moonstone** by Wilkie Collin
- **The Prisoner of Zenda** by Anth
- **Sense and Sensibility** by Jane Austen

LEVEL 5

- **The Invisible Man** by H.G. Wells
- **Shakespeare's Tragedies** by William Shakespeare
- **Shakespeare's Comedies** by William Shakespeare
- **A Tale of Two Cities** by Charles Dickens
- **Vanity Fair** by William Makepeace Thackeray
- **Pride and Prejudice** by Jane Austen
- **Moby Dick** by Herman Melville
- **The Importance of Being Earnest** by Oscar Wilde
- **More Tales of Mystery and Imagination** by Edgar Allan Poe
- **The Hound of the Baskervilles** by Sir Arthur Conan Doyle

LEVEL 6

- **Wuthering Heights** by Emily Jane Brontë
- **Great Expectations** by Charles Dickens
- **Nicholas Nickleby** by Charles Dickens
- **The Three Musketeers** by Alexandre Dumas, père
- **The Phantom of the Opera** by Gaston Leroux
- **Jane Eyre** by Charlotte Brontë
- **Tess of the D'Urbervilles** by Thomas Hardy
- **Classic American Short Stories** by Various Authors
- **Classic British Short Stories** by Various Authors
- **The War of the Worlds** by H.G. Wells